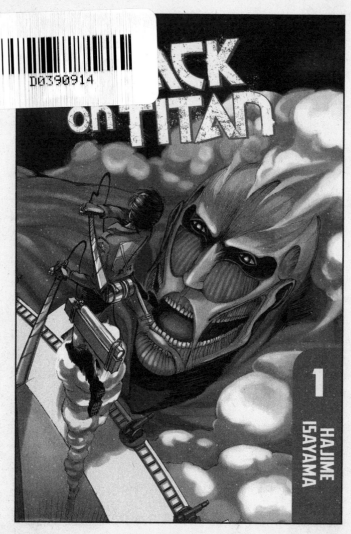

For millennia, human beings ruled the natural world. But a century ago, everything changed when the maneating Titans appeared. Giant, grotesque parodies of the human form, these sexless monsters proved nearly impossible to kill, and were driven by a single desire: to consume human beings. The survivors took refuge behind three concentric walls, and as the years passed, grew complacent. Now a young boy, Eren Yeager, yearns to explore the world beyond the walls. But what began as a childish dream will become an all too real nightmare when a Titan finally knocks a hole in the outermost wall, and the Titans once again threaten to wipe out humanity...

Vols. 1-15 now available
Colossal Edition 1 (Vols. 1-5 omnibus) now available
Colossal Edition 2 (Vols. 6-10 omnibus) coming September 2015

...EREN SAID...

YEAH. I HAVE TO SEE A PATIENT TWO TOWNS UP.

HUH? DAD, YOU'RE GOING OUT **NOW?**

M-MIKASA!! I TOLD YOU NOT TO TELL THEM!

EREN!!

...HE WANTS TO JOIN THE SURVEY CORPS.

...

Y-YES, I KNOW!!

DO YOU KNOW HOW MANY PEOPLE HAVE DIED BECAUSE THEY DARED TO VENTURE OUTSIDE THE WALL?!

WHAT ARE YOU THINKING?!

EREN...

WHY DO YOU WANT TO GO **OUTSIDE?**

I HATE THE IDEA OF SPENDING MY WHOLE LIFE...

...INSIDE THE WALL, IGNORANT OF WHAT'S HAPPENING IN THE WORLD OUTSIDE!!

AND BESIDES...

IF THERE'S NO ONE TO CARRY ON...

...EVERYONE WHO DIED UP TO NOW WILL HAVE DIED IN VAIN!

WAIT... HONEY!

WELL, I'D BETTER BE GOING. THE BOAT LEAVES SOON.

...I SEE...

!!

IT DOESN'T MATTER WHAT ANYONE SAYS. THERE'S NO HOLDING BACK AN INQUISITIVE MIND.

CARLA...

TALK SOME SENSE INTO YOUR SON!!

...THAT I'VE BEEN KEEPING SECRET ALL THIS TIME.

WHEN I GET HOME... I'LL SHOW YOU WHAT'S IN THE BASEMENT...

R-REALLY?!

...

...

EREN...

...WHAT?

EREN...

"FOOLISH"...?!

WHAT ?!

...DO ANYTHING AS FOOLISH AS JOINING THE SURVEY CORPS!

I WON'T LET YOU...

EREN...

....

...

...ARE THE REAL FOOLS!

THE WAY I SEE IT... PEOPLE WHO ARE SATISFIED LIVING LIKE CAGED BIRDS...

I WILL!

...SO HELP HIM OUT IF HE GETS IN TROUBLE.

THAT BOY IS FOOLHARDY...

MIKASA...

...HE PUNCHED ME...

...AND CALLED ME A "HERETIC".

...SHOULD EVENTUALLY GO TO THE OUTSIDE WORLD...

SO WHEN I SAID THE HUMAN RACE...

PEOPLE ARE AFRAID THAT IF WE GO OUT CARELESSLY, **THEY** COULD GET IN.

WELL... IT'S BECAUSE WE'VE LIVED HERE PEACEFULLY INSIDE THE WALL FOR 100 YEARS NOW.

DAMN IT, WHY DO PEOPLE FROWN ON EVEN THE SLIGHTEST MENTION OF WANTING TO GO "OUTSIDE"?

BUT I WONDER IF THAT'S THE ONLY REASON...

...YOU'RE RIGHT ABOUT THAT.

WE CAN DO WHAT WE WANT WITH THEM, RIGHT?

THEY'RE **OUR** LIVES!

...NOT!

AB-SOLUTE-LY...

IN OTHER WORDS, THE KING IS A COWARD!

ROYAL GOVERNMENT POLICY SAYS THAT EVEN HAVING AN INTEREST IN GOING TO THE OUTSIDE WORLD IS TABOO.

I DON'T REMEMBER AGREEING TO KEEP IT A SECRET.

THAT REMINDS ME, THANKS A LOT FOR RATTING ME OUT TO MOM AND DAD!!

NO WAY.

...

!

...NATURALLY...

...THEY WEREN'T PLEASED.

OF COURSE...

SO... HOW'D THEY TAKE IT?

...BUT COME ON, IT'S DANGEROUS.

LOOK, I KNOW HOW YOU FEEL...

W-WHAT THE HELL?! ARE YOU TELLING ME TO GIVE UP ON IT TOO?!

...THERE'S NO GUARANTEE THAT THEY WON'T BREAK THROUGH IT TODAY, FOR EXAMPLE.

JUST BECAUSE THE WALL HASN'T BEEN BREACHED IN 100 YEARS...

I MEAN, FOR SURE, I THINK THE PEOPLE WHO BELIEVE WE'LL BE SAFE INSIDE THIS WALL FOREVER HAVE A SCREW LOOSE.

ARMIN, WHAT IS IT...?!

TA TA TA

SWISH

H-HEY... WHAT THE HECK ARE YOU LOOKING AT?!

DASH

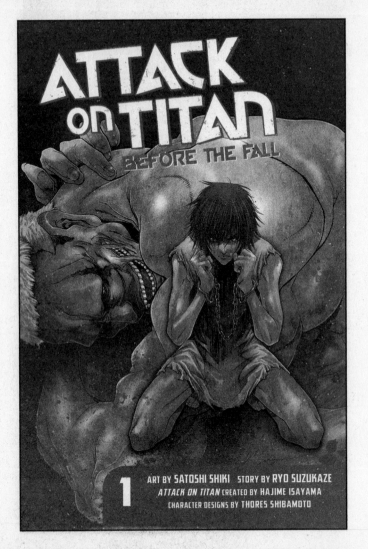

A prequel series to the number one bestseller in Japan. Humanity has learned to live in com-
placency behind its high walls, protected from the giant Titans. But when a Titan-worshipping
cult opens one of the gates, a Titan wreaks havoc, consuming the cultists. After the rampage is
over, two young Survey Corps members are shocked to discover a pregnant woman's partially
digested corpse - with her baby still alive inside it! What will the fate of this "child of the
Titans" be? And how will humanity learn to cope with the Titan threat?

Winner of the Diamond Gem Award for Manga of the Year, 2014!
Vols. 1-4 now available
Vol. 5 coming in August 2015

THE FALL OF
WALL MARIA.

...ON WHICH HUMANITY LOST...

THE FATEFUL DAY

...A THIRD OF ITS SAFE HARBOR...

BUT FEW KNEW OF THE FACT THAT **THEY**
ONCE BREACHED OUR WALLS 70 YEARS AGO...

...FOR DESPITE THE MANY VICTIMS OF THAT
DISASTER, THE ROYAL GOVERNMENT FORBADE
THE PEOPLE TO SPEAK OF IT, AND ERASED ALL
TRACES OF IT FROM RECORD...

BUT IT REALLY DID HAPPEN.

ATTACK on TITAN
BEFORE THE FALL
Trailer
...OF HUMANITY'S TERRIBLE FOE...
...AND CARVED IT DEEP...
...INTO THEIR HEARTS!!!

ZMF..

ZMF..

IL..

WHA
...?

A...
TITAN
...?

ZMF...

ZMF...

BUT
HOW
...?!

AT THIS TIME...

...HUMANITY HAD NO WAY TO
FIGHT THE TITANS.

*This "Trailer" was originally run in the October 2013
issue of Monthly Shonen Sirius as a prologue.

1

ADACHITOKA

NORAGAMI
STRAY GOD

Divine intervention for sale!

Yato is a homeless god. He doesn't even have a shrine, not to mention worshippers! So to achieve his ambitious goals, he's set up a service to help those in need (for a small fee), hoping he'll eventually raise enough money to build himself the lavish temple of his dreams. Of course, he can't afford to be picky, so Yato accepts all kinds of jobs, from finding lost kittens to helping a student overcome bullies at school.

Hit anime now available from FUNimation!
Vols. 1-4 now available
Vol. 5 coming June 2015

CHAPTER 1: THE MAN IN THE SWEATSUIT

HUFF, HUFF, UFF!

HUFF HUFF!

YATO-SAN, YOU PUT YOUR NUMBER *HERE?!*

CALL IT PROSELY-TIZING.

WHERE DID THEY COME FROM...?

WHO *ARE* THEY?!

HUFF, HUFF!

HUFF!

I AM A GOD.

HEH HEH!

OVER-WHELMED BY MY SUPREME PRES-ENCE?

HE'S A SCHIZO!

WELL, IT'S TRUE, ISN'T IT?! AND LEARN TO READ THE ROOM!

TOMONE, NOT IN FRONT OF THE CUSTOM-ERS!

WE'RE HAVING A SALE!

DON'T WORR HE'S REAL! BL HE IS AT THE VERY BOTTO OF THE BOTTO OF THE DIVIN HIERARCHY.

SO YOUR PROBLEM IS BULLIES, RIGHT?

I'LL CUT 'EM TO PIECES FOR YOU.

YATO-SAN! NOT THAT AGAIN...

JUST TELL ME WHOSE HEAD YOU WANT ME TO BRING YOU...

EH, DON'T MIND HER.

KEEP TALKING LIKE THAT, AND YOU REALLY WILL FALL INTO DEPRAVITY!

AW, COME ON. SLAYING'S THE ONLY THING I'M GOOD AT.

SHE CAN COME LATE, IGNORE THE UNIFORM RULES...

AND THE TEACHERS WON'T EVEN GET MAD— THEY'LL JUST BE GLAD SHE'S ACTUALLY HERE.

THANKS FOR LUNCH!

I KNOW, RIGHT?

SHE SHOULD JUST STAYE IN THE NURSE OFFICE DAY.

SHE JUST HAS TO STOP COMING TO SCHOOL FOR A WHILE, AND THEY'LL TREAT HER SPECIAL.

JINGLE

JINGLE

NOW SHE JUST HAS TO SLIT HER WRIST, AND SHE'LL BE UNSTOPPABLE.

YOU'RE AWFUL!

MIDTERM TESTS

1. LANGUAGE ARTS 8:45-9:30
2. MATH 9:40-10:45
3. ENGLISH 10:35-11:20

NOV 15

GIRLS ARE SCARY!

CHEER

CREAK

IT'S ALMOST TIME FOR ENTRANCE EXAMS.

I DON'T HAVE TIME TO WASTE WORRYING ABOUT A FREAK LIKE YOU.

しく SOB しく SOB しく SOB しく SOB

SHUT UP! PUBLIC PROPERTY IS MY PROPERTY!!

WHAT THE— IT'S ALL SINGLE-PLY!

I have a sensitive ass, I'll have you know!

YATO-SAN, THAT BELONGS TO THE SCHOOL!

THUMP

THUMP

THUMP

THUMP

BUMP

WHY DOES THIS ONLY HAPPEN TO MUTSUMI...

HNN

HIC

しく SOB しく SOB しく SOB

A-AAH!!

YATO-SAN, READ THE ROOM!!

YU!! BLECH

TALKING ABOUT YOURSELF IN THE THIRD PERSON? WHAT AN EGO.

AND LOOK.

UGH, WHY BOTHER? SHE'S JUST A STUPID KID.

I TOLD YOU, BE *POLITE* TO CUS-TOMERS.

...HUH?

LIFE AND DEATH ARE LIKE LIGHT AND SHADOW.

THEY'RE BOTH ALWAYS THERE.

BUT PEOPLE DON'T LIKE THINKING ABOUT DEATH, SO SUBCONSCIOUSLY, THEY ALWAYS LOOK AWAY FROM IT.

SHEEE!

F...FAR SHORE...?

YOUR PEOPLE CALL IT "THE AFTERLIFE."

THAT CREATES BLIND SPOTS. GODS, DEMONS—EVERYTHING SUPERNATURAL LIVES IN THOSE BLIND SPOTS.

THEY'RE HIDING IN THE DEAD SPACE, BUT THEY ARE ALWAYS NEARBY.

...

AND WHEN YOU'RE WEAK, THEY POUNCE.

ONCE THEY CATCH YOU,

THE EVIL INSIDE YOU TAKES OVER.

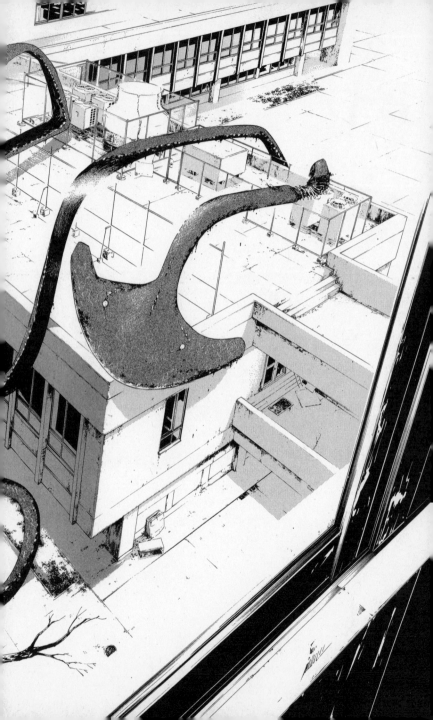

HAAAAHH

IT'S HELLA HUGE!!

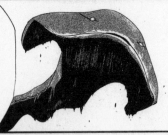

BECAUSE IT'S IN THEIR BLIND SPOTS.

WHY DOESN'T ANYONE SEE IT?!

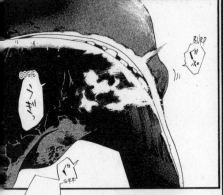

BURP

OOGIE

GRR

DROP DEAD...

SPLURCH

As a child, Thorfinn sat at the feet of the great Leif Ericson and thrilled to wild tales of a land far to the west. But his youthful fantasies were shattered by a mercenary raid. Raised by the Vikings who murdered his family, Thorfinn became a terrifying warrior, forever seeking to kill the band's leader, Askeladd, and avenge his father. Sustaining Throfinn through his ordeal are his pride in his family and his dreams of a fertile westward land, a land without war or slavery...the land Leif called *Vinland*.

Deluxe hardcover 2-in-1 editions with exclusive author Q&As and bonus story! Books One to Five now available

MUST BE A SIGNAL OF SOME KIND.

MOST LIKELY...

ANOTHER ONE.

THAT MAKES FOUR.

BE ON GUARD.

THEY'LL TRY SOMETHING DIFFERENT TOMORROW.

YES SIR!

...

MAKING CONTACT WITH ANOTHER COMPANY, PERHAPS?

THAT'LL BE THOR-FINN.

ONE HIGH, THREE LOW.

FSHH...

GREAT. THAT'S ALL WE NEED TO KNOW.

THEY'L BE STRIKIN AT SUI UP.

WE MUST BE OVER THE PEAK BEFORE THE MOON RISES.

ON THE DOUBLE, LADS!

DSSHHHH

WHOOO...

WHOO...

DAHH!!

CAN'T TAKE ANNYMORE A'DIS!!

BSHH...

DGSSHHH

STANDIN' SHIP GUARD ALLA WAY DOWN HERE?! PAH!

HOW'S A MAN GUNNA MAKE A NAME FOR HISSELF AWAY FROM BATTLE?!

OUR ARMY'S SCRATCHIN' TOOTH AN' NAIL CROSS THE FALLS, I HEAR

FERGEDDIT, YE'LL ONLY GET YERSELF KILT.

I LEFF HOME AN' TOLL EVERYONE I'D BE A KNIGHT!

PUT ME OUT ON THE FIELD AN' LEMME FIGHT, YA FAT PIG!!

LEAST WE'RE SAFE DOWN HERE.

CRUNK

CRAK SWASH

WHOOSH WHOOSH

 IF YA SO AFRAIDA FIGHTIN', WHYJA FOLLA ME TO BATTLE?!

 PEH! COWARD.

YOU BEEN YELLA SINCE WE WAS KIDS.

 PAT PAT

WHAAT?

WHAT'S DIS NOW, TUBBY?

 CUZ I'M CON-CERNED FOR YA.

...

 LOOK UP THERE...

WUSS ALL THE MUTTERIN' ABOUT?!

 I DON'T NEED NO STINKIN' BABYSIDDER!!

I WUZ DA ROWDIEST BRAWLER IN DA VILLAGE, AND YOU AIN'T NEVER EVEN BEEN INNA FIGHT...

 ?

 RIGHT NEAR THE PEAK

SOMETHIN' POPPED UP FOR A SEC...

 *MURMUR* *MURMUR*

GRAH... GRAH...

AAAHHH

A... DRAGON ON THE MOUNTAIN-TOP!!

IT'S A DRAGON!!

...DRAGON.

...

OH, BUGGER ME...

A DRAGON CLIMBING THE MOUNTAIN?

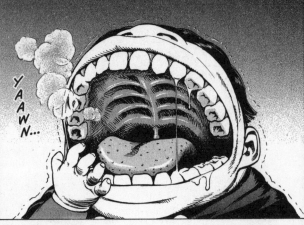

YAAWN...

AHH...

YES, MY LORD. THE SHIP GUARDS SENT A REPORT LAST NIGHT.

BUT ENOUGH ABOUT THAT...

OY!!

I'VE ALWAYS WANTED TO SEE A DRAGON!

HA HA HA!

IT IS AN ILL OMEN, MY LIEGE.

62

YOUR FRIENDS ARE NO-SHOWS.

THE SUN IS OUT AND RISING.

YOU'LL SEE SOON ENOUGH.

JUST GET ON WITH THE ATTACK, FAT-ASS.

IT SEEMS YOUR HEAD WILL BE THE CENTER-PIECE OF OUR VICTORY FEAST TONIGHT, BOY!!

PREPARE TO ATTACK!!

YOU JUST INSULTED ME, DIDN'T YOU?

I'VE AN EAR FOR THESE THINGS.

CHEEKY WHELP...

AYE!!

IT'S
OILING!!

YEOW!!

AAGH

PSHH

EEEK

SPASHHH

RAHHHHH

SILENCE THOSE ARROWS!

I WANT LADDERS ON THE WEST FACE, CASUALTIES BE DAMNED!

HEY, INTER-PRETER.

WHICH ONE'S THE ENEMY LEADER?

...GOOD.

FWEET

PWEEP

FSHH

CREAAK

RAHHH

SEE THE ONE WITH THE FEATHERED HELM? THAT'S HIM.

AHH.

AAAA—RGH

THE BOY RUNS OFF, THE FORTRESS STILL STANDS, AND THERE ARE NO ALLIES!!

WHAT'S WRONG WITH THIS STUPID ARMY?!

DMM DMM DMM

RAHHH

LET ME BE CLEAR, WE ARE *NOT* GOING HOME WHEN THE SNOWS COME!!

WE'RE HERE UNTIL THIS FORTRESS HAS—

ARE YOU ME OR SCARE-CROWS?!

DON'T JUST STAND THERE, *DO* SOME-THING!!

DMM DMM DMM

RAHHHH...

WHAT YOU HEAR IS *FIGHTING*, WHICH IS WHAT YOU OUGHT TO BE DOING RIGHT NOW!!

N-NO, MY LORD, IT'S COMING CLOSER!!

I HEAR SOMETHING STRANGE...

DMM DMM DMM DMM

Y-YES, BUT, MY LORD...

ARE YOU LISTENING TO ME?!

DMM DMM DMM DMM

DMM DMM

THERE... HEAR IT?!

?

71

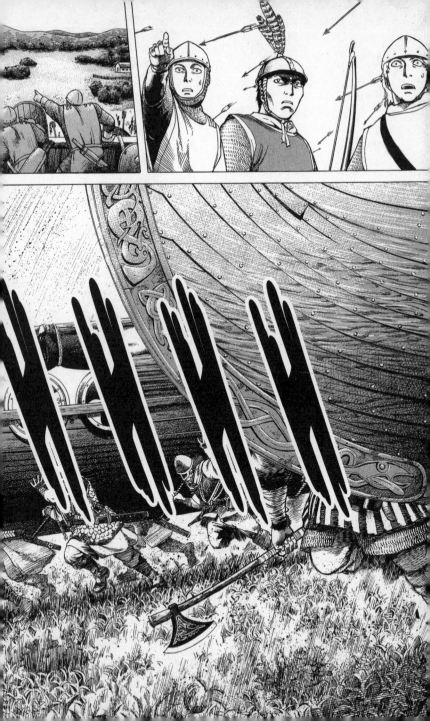

A superhero like none you've ever seen, from the creator of *Gantz*!

Ichiro Inuyashiki is an old man. His ungrateful family ignores him and strangers are disgusted by him. Then, just after learning he has terminal cancer, a blinding light in the night sky strikes the earth where Ichiro stands. He wakes up to find himself unscathed, but he soon starts to notice that something's… different. Maybe this is his chance to become a man worthy of respect. Unless, that is, someone else out there is experiencing these same "changes"…

A science fiction action story full of twists and turns, in extra-large editions with color pages! Vol. 1 coming August 2015

...YOUNG MAIDENS...

FALL IN LOVE...

...IS SHORRRT...

LIIIFE...

OH...

AH!

YOU HAVE TO KEEP HER OUTSIDE IF YOU'RE NOT GOING TO TRAIN HER PROPERLY.

HANAKO POOPED INSIDE THE HOUSE, JUST SO YOU KNOW.

-NO-HING...

NO...

DO YOU HAVE SOMETHING TO SAY?

WHAT?

?

IF I ACTUALLY... TOLD THEM...

WOULD THEY CRY FOR ME?

WOULD THEY... CRY ABOUT IT...?

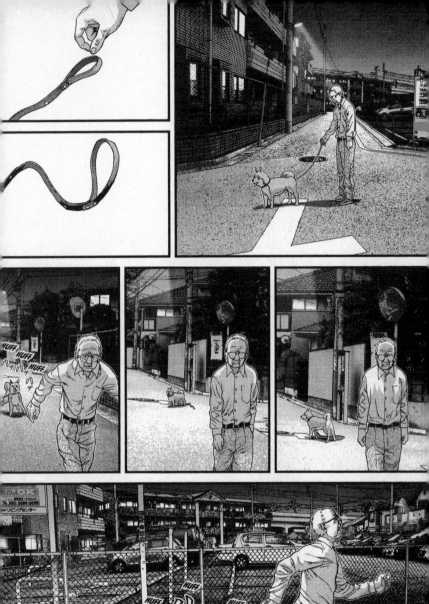
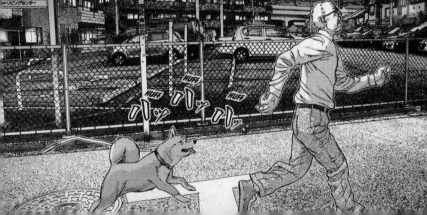

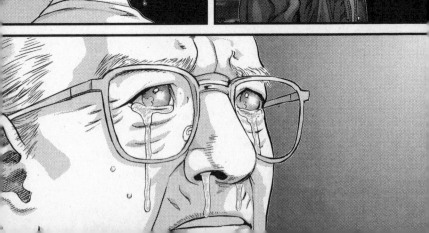

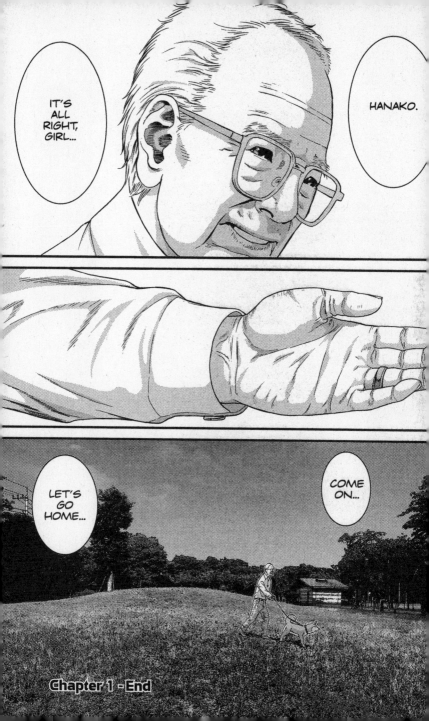

Chapter 1 - End

ringing music back to a life in monotone

osei Arima was a piano prodigy until his cruel taskmaster of a mother died suddenly, changing s life forever. Driven by his pain to abandon piano, Kosei now lives in a monotonous, colorless orld. Having resigned himself to a bland life, he is surprised when he meets Kaori Miyazono, a olinist with an unorthodox style. Can she bring Kosei back to music, and back to life?

Hit anime streaming now from Aniplex USA!
Vol. 1 now available
Vol. 2 coming in June 2015!

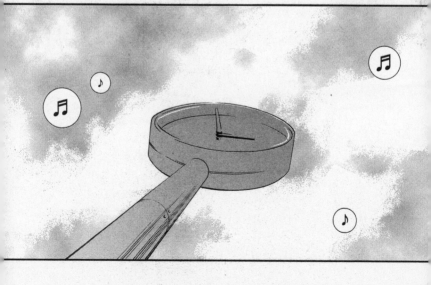

"EVERYTHING I SAW,

EVERYTHING I HEARD,

EVERYTHING AROUND ME

EVERYTHING I FELT.

AROUND ME

STARTED TO FILL WITH GLORIOUS COLOR."

"THE WORLD

BEGAN TO SPARKLE!"

HUH?

THAT'S WEIRD.

IT WORKS FOR PAZU.

WHEN IT COMES TO MUSIC, THERE ARE NO BORDERS BETWEEN COUNTRIES, RACE, OR SPECIES.

FLEX

YOU'RE PLAYING A MELODICA!

IT HAS TO BE A BUGLE!

A TRUMPET!

WAAH

I HAVE A RECORDER!

WAAH

'LL
LAY
STA-
ETS!

LET'S ALL TRY IT TOGETHER.

-108-

THEY MAKE SUCH A BEAUTIFUL PICTURE.

A Kodansha Comics Trade Paperback Original

Attack on Titan copyright © 2010 Hajime Isayama
English translation copyright © 2012 Hajime Isayama
Translation: Sheldon Drzka
Lettering: Steve Wands

...ck on Titan: Before the Fall copyright © 2013 Hajime Isayama/Ryo Suzukaze/Satoshi Shiki
English translation copyright © 2014 Hajime Isayama/Ryo Suzukaze/Satoshi Shiki
Translation: Stephen Paul
Lettering: Steve Wands
Editing: Ben Applegate

Noragami: Stray God copyright © 2011 Adachitoka
English translation copyright © 2014 Adachitoka
Translation: Alethea Nibley & Athena Nibley
Lettering: Lys Blakeslee

Vinland Saga copyright © 2006 Makoto Yukimura
English translation copyright © 2013 Makoto Yukimura
Translation: Stephen Paul
Lettering: Scott O. Brown
Editing: Ben Applegate

Inuyashiki copyright © 2014 Hiroya Oku
English translation copyright © 2015 Hiroya Oku
Translation: Stephen Paul
Lettering: Scott O. Brown
Editing: Ajani Oloye

Your Lie in April copyright © 2011 Naoshi Arakawa
English translation copyright © 2015 Naoshi Arakawa
Translation: Alethea Nibley & Athena Nibley
Lettering: Scott O. Brown
Editing: Ben Applegate

Cover designs of Kodansha Comics editions by Phil Balsman

All rights reserved.

Published in the United States by Kodansha Comics, an imprint of
Kodansha USA Publishing, LLC, New York.

Publication rights for this English edition arranged through Kodansha Ltd, Tokyo.

ISBN 978-1-63236-204-9

Printed in the United States of America.

www.kodanshacomics.com

9 8 7 6 5 4 3 2 1